This book belongs to:

_____

- -

_____

Date:

_____

- -

_____

What Can You Do...

Catholic Easy Reader
and Keepsake Journal

Nancy Nicholson

For Little Folks

www.forlittlefolks.com

Dedicated to Catholic homeschooling children everywhere

ISBN: 978-0-9771236-4-3

Printed by Sheridan Books, Inc.
Chelsea, Michigan   April 2014
Print code: 359350

For Little Folks
P.O. Box 571
Dresden, OH 43821
www.forlittlefolks.com

Distributed by
Catholic Heritage Curricula
P.O. Box 579090, Modesto, CA 95357
1-800-490-7713   www.chcweb.com

Contents

Introduction and Instructions

The reading level in this book is suitable for the child who has completed *Little Stories for Little Folks,* Level 3. [For the child who is learning to read using a different reading program, *Little Stories for Little Folks: Catholic Phonics Readers* also offers further reading practice.]

As the child reads stories of other children living out the Corporal and Spiritual Works of Mercy, he is both challenged and invited to include his own responses to serving Christ in others. These personal accounts, to be written and/or illustrated in the pages provided, not only give the child a special "ownership" of his book but also create a precious and treasured record from your child's first grade year.

[To preserve the child's enthusiasm at this beginning writing level, it is best to allow him or her to write without correction.]

"For I was hungry and you gave Me to eat...

as you did it to one of the least of these brethren, you did it to Me."

Matt. 25:35 & 40

Corporal Works of Mercy

feed the hungry

give drink to the thirsty

clothe the naked

shelter the homeless

visit the sick

visit those in prison

bury the dead

Spiritual Works of Mercy

instruct the ignorant

counsel the doubtful

admonish the sinner

comfort the sorrowful

forgive injuries

bear wrongs patiently

pray for the living and the dead

1
What Can You Do to Feed the Hungry?

Bakhita's Idea

Bakhita heard Mama in the bedroom, singing softly to the new baby.

Bakhita and Patsy were in the dining room, sitting down to breakfast. Mama had put peanut

New words: idea   thought

butter toast and oranges on the table for the girls. She asked Bakhita to pour the milk. Then she left to feed the baby.

Bakhita carefully filled the glasses with milk. She was glad that she knew how to help.

The girls said the blessing. They started to eat the sweet oranges and toast.

Yum! Peanut butter toast was Bakhita's favorite. She licked the peanut butter off the top of the toast, and thought about Mama.

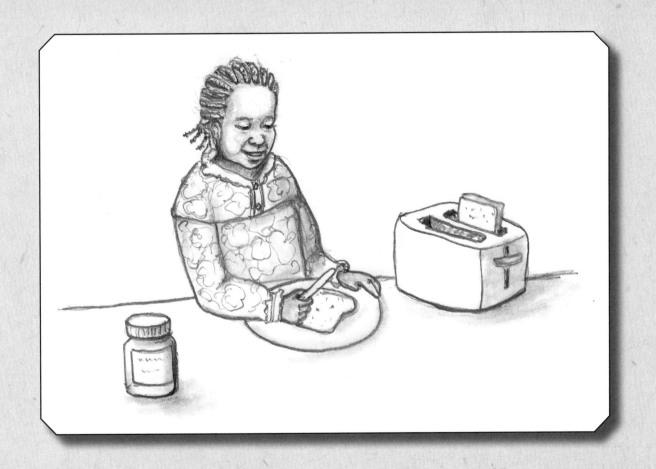

Mama was up early with the baby, but Mama had no time to eat. And now she was feeding the baby.

The new baby will have a full tummy, thought Bakhita. Patsy and I will have full tummies. But Mama will be hungry.

I am the biggest sister. I am six, and I can pour milk for Patsy. I can put peanut butter on toast. And I can peel oranges, too.

I can surprise Mama. I can fix oranges and toast for her. I will fix breakfast in bed for Mama.

And that's just what Bakhita did to feed the hungry. What can *you* do to feed the hungry?

2

What Can You Do to Feed the Hungry?

Tim's Idea

Monica tugged hard on Mama's skirt. "My tummy hungry!" she said, patting her little tummy.

"Tim, please can you make a snack for Monica?" said Mother. "Maybe some cheese? I need to finish making these pies for the church bake sale."

"Sure, Mom," said Tim. "But I bet Monica's not as hungry as that family you read about this morning."

Mom had read about a family that lived far across the sea, in a different land. They were very poor. Sometimes they had no food to eat all day. No breakfast. No lunch. No dinner.

Our family is blessed to have so much, Tim thought as he cut some cheese for his little sister.

Jesus said to feed the hungry. I'd like to go help that other family,

Tim thought, but I cannot ride my bike that far. And I don't have any money.

Someday, when I am big and have a job, I am going to help that family far away. I want to feed the hungry like Jesus said.

Monica reached her little hands up. She took the snack that Tim had made for her. She stuffed a big bite into her mouth and smiled her best "thank you" smile.

Tim smiled back at his little sister. Someday, I will feed the hungry far away, he thought. But today, I can feed the hungry here.

When someone is

hungry, I can

14

3

What Can You Do When Someone Is Sad?

Jon's Idea

Under the swing, the dirt was hot and dry. Jon sat on the swing. He dragged his feet on the ground. His bare toes made lines in the dust.

All the big kids had gone to the park without him. Jon was alone and sad. No one else was in the back yard. No one played at the creek. Even the yard and creek seemed lonely.

Jon used to see Grandpa and Grandma fishing together at the creek almost every day. They held hands and talked and fished.

But then Grandma died. Now, Grandpa just stayed in his house next door. Most days, he didn't even pull up the window shades. Grandpa is more sad and lonely than I am, Jon thought. He misses Grandma. Then Jon had an idea. I know a way to make Grandpa happy!

Soon Jon was on Grandpa's porch. He knocked loudly. The window shade lifted a little, and Grandpa's sad eyes peeked at Jon. Slowly, the door opened.

"See what I dug in the garden, Grandpa?" Jon held up a rusty can, full of wiggly red worms for Grandpa to see. "Please can you go fishing with me?"

Grandpa looked into the can of wiggly worms. His eyes began to twinkle, and a smile spread across his face.

"I don't like to fish alone," Grandpa said. "But with all those worms to keep us company, we won't be lonely, will we?

"Wait here, and I'll get my pole."

Why, I'm not sad anymore, Jon thought as he waited. I wanted to make Grandpa happy, but now I'm happy, too.

And that's what Jon did when someone was sad. What can *you* do when someone is sad?

4
What Can You Do When Someone Is Sad?

Mike's Idea

Mama carefully put baby Emma in the baby sitter's arms.

"I won't be gone long; I hope the baby won't fuss. Maybe you can feed her now. Then she will think about food instead of Mama," Mama said as she went out.

Baby Emma saw the door shut. Mama was gone!

Emma began to wail.

The baby sitter put Emma in her little seat at the table. She softly patted baby Emma's back.

The baby cried, "Ma-ma!" She did not want to eat. She wanted Mama.

"Mike, it's time to eat," called the baby sitter. "Maybe if you sit by Emma she will stop crying. Maybe she will eat her lunch."

"Sure," said Mike. He sat next to Emma. He took a long noodle from his plate. He stuck the noodle to the end of his nose. He swung his head from side to side. "Emma, look at the elly-funt!"

Emma stopped crying. She clapped her hands and smiled; the baby sitter frowned at the noodle on Mike's nose.

Mike put the noodle back on his plate; Emma sobbed, "Ma-ma!"

The baby sitter tried to feed the baby. Emma screamed; Emma did not eat.

Mike pulled his T-shirt up over his chin. He made turtle faces. Emma wiggled and giggled. The baby sitter smiled.

Mike tickled Emma's baby toes. Emma wiggled and giggled; then she began to eat.

The baby sitter turned to Mike. "You made Emma happy again. I'm glad you helped Emma. You helped me, too."

And that's what Mike did when someone was sad. What can *you* do when someone is sad?

When someone is
sad, I can

28

5

How Can You Give Drink to the Thirsty?

Karl's Idea

Back and forth across the front lawn, Matt pushed the lawn mower. The mower growled and spit grass clippings across the yard. Back and forth, back and forth, Matt pushed the mower in the hot sun.

"Daddy, please, please may I mow the lawn like Matt?" begged Karl as he followed Daddy outside.

Dad smiled at Karl. "You are just six, son. When you are as big as Matt, you can mow the lawn.

"But you can help a different way. You can rake the grass." Dad handed a rake to Karl.

Karl took the rake. He raked up one little pile of grass and stopped. I am so hot and thirsty, Karl thought. This is a lot of work.

Back and forth, back and forth, Matt kept pushing the mower in the summer heat.

Karl slowly dragged the rake over the grass clippings. I wish I could run the mower, he thought. It is too hot to rake grass, and I am very, very thirsty. I think I will go get a glass of cold water.

Karl dropped his rake on the lawn. As he walked to the house, Matt passed him, pushing the mower. Then Karl saw Matt wipe his sweating, red face.

Matt has been working a lot longer than I have, thought Karl. I bet he is way more thirsty than I am. I will get him a glass of cold water first. Then I will get one for myself.

And that is how Karl gave drink to the thirsty. What can *you* do when someone is thirsty?

When someone is

thirsty, I can

6

What Can You Do to Clothe the Naked?

Todd's Idea

"You grew so much last year! Now we have a big box of clothes to send to Mexico," Mother said happily. She neatly put Todd's too-small pants and shirts inside the big box.

"We can give this to Sister Rita to take on her next trip to Mexico," Mother said as she taped the big box shut.

"I just wish we had more to send. Sister Rita says there are many poor children who have almost no clothes."

"We can give them all the clothes in my closet, Mom," Todd offered. He looked down at the shirt and pants he was wearing. "I will just keep these."

Mother smiled and gave Todd a big hug. "You are thinking of others, but you need clothes to wear, too. Let's both think and pray about this.

"Maybe there is another way to get more clothes," Mother said as she took the box into the laundry room.

Todd thought and thought. He asked Jesus to give him an idea. Then he jumped up and ran to the laundry room.

PLEdse
Put Good clothes
for Poor
Children Here

"I know, Mom! I will ask Father if we can put a box by every door in the church. I will print a big note on each box. It will say, 'Please put good clothes for poor children here.' Then Sister Rita can help more children."

And that is how Todd helped clothe the naked.

7

What Can You Do to Clothe the Naked?

Nita's Idea

"We are going to Holy Mass at San Agustin this morning!" Mother called from the living room. "Hurry and dress; we don't want to be late."

"That means we are going to Manila today," Nita told her little brother. "Can you get dressed by yourself?"

"I can dress myself," said three-year-old Rafa.

"I can put on my shirt."

Nita took her best lacy pink dress from the bedroom closet. She quickly pulled it over her head and began doing the buttons.

"Nita, I can't see!" Rafa cried from somewhere inside his shirt.

"That's because your head is in the sleeve," Nita giggled.

"You must put your head in the neck hole."

Rafa pulled his shirt off and dropped it on the floor. "I will put on my pants. I can dress myself."

Rafa sat on the floor and put his feet in the pant leg. He tugged and pulled. Then Rafa stood up, but he did not walk.

"I can't walk!" Rafa moaned.

"That's because you have two feet in one pant leg," Nita giggled again.

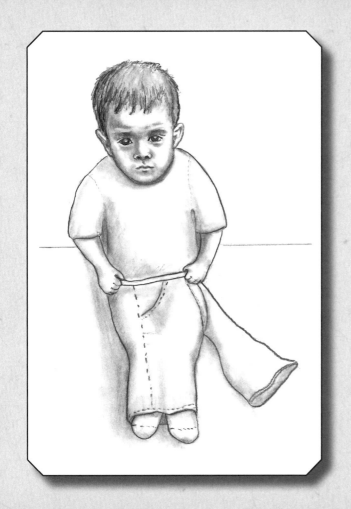

Rafa folded his arms across his chest and frowned. "I am not going to wear a shirt or pants today."

"You can't go to Holy Mass without a shirt or pants. I will help you dress for Holy Mass."

And that's how Nita helped clothe the naked. What can *you* do to clothe the naked?

45

When someone

needs clothes, I can

8

What Can You Do to Visit the Sick?

Teresa's Idea

Kateri rolled over in bed and rubbed her neck. My throat is sore and I feel hot. I wish I didn't have to stay in bed, she thought. Being sick isn't fun.

Just then, Kateri's little sister Teresa peeked her head around the bedroom door. "Are you awake?" she asked.

Teresa crawled onto the bed and began to bounce up and down. "Please may I play with your new doll house?" she asked.

"Since you have to stay in bed and the doll house is in the family room, you can't play with it anyway."

Kateri nodded sadly at Teresa. "Yes, you may play with it. The doll family is inside the doll house, and I think the tiny table and chairs are in the toy box.

"Just stop bouncing, please. It makes me dizzy."

"I'm sorry, and thanks, Kateri!" Teresa bounced off the bed and was gone in a flash.

Kateri wished she could play with the doll house, too. Being sick is not fun, but I will try to offer it up, Kateri thought.

Soon, there was an odd sound in the hallway. Teresa was pushing a big plastic tub in front of her, across the carpet and into the bedroom.

In the tub was the doll house, with the doll family lined up on the roof, waving stiffly at Kateri.

"You can't come to the doll house," Teresa said, "so the doll house is coming to you."

Teresa made the doll family march across the bed to a smiling Kateri. "We can play here. There is room on the bed for all of us.

"And I promise I won't bounce."

9

What Can You Do to Visit the Sick?

Martin's Idea

The church hall is full of noisy children. A Christmas tree stands in one corner. A table with cookies and hot chocolate stands next to it.

Teesha and Martin's Sunday School class is all dressed up for the Living Nativity.

New words: Joseph   Christmas

The Nativity is going to be on the church lawn. People driving down the street will see the Christmas story as they drive past.

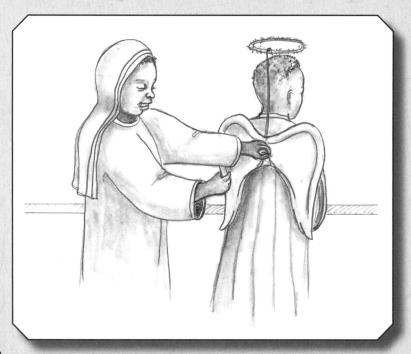

"Martin, your wings are falling off. Stand still and I will fix them for you." Teesha Maree snapped the wings to the back of her brother's angel costume.

Teesha rocked a Baby Jesus doll in her arms. "Joseph" stood beside her.

After the Living Nativity, there will be a Christmas party in the church hall. But now, the children march down the steps to go outdoors.

"Ow! The donkey stepped on me!" Martin hopped on one foot. "Who is in the donkey costume?"

"Sorry," Rob said from inside the furry costume. "I can't see very well. And this is not my day.

"My grandpa always comes to see the Living Nativity, but he can't this time. He broke his hip and has to stay home in bed. Dad said he was very upset."

Martin stepped outside onto the lawn. He and Rob stood beside the Wise Men. The Wise Men made Martin think of bringing gifts to Baby Jesus in His little manger bed. Beds made him think of Rob's sad grandpa, at home in bed.

"Hey, I know what we can do!" Martin cried. "We can have a Living Nativity at your grandpa's!"

"We don't have to go to the Christmas party. After we are done here, I will ask Dad if you and 'Joseph' can go with us in our van. Maybe they will even let us take some cookies. We can make a Christmas party at your grandpa's!"

And that is just what they did.

10

What Can You Do to Visit the Sick?

Zeke's Idea

Zeke patted the lump in his pocket and smiled as he skipped up the driveway to his house.

Old Mrs. Frank lived next door. She was not very strong, so every Sunday Zeke took the garbage out for her.

Today, Mrs. Frank had given Zeke the lump in his pocket. The lump was Zeke's favorite lollipop: grape, with chocolate in the middle. Zeke smiled again. I will save this lollipop and eat it after dinner, he thought.

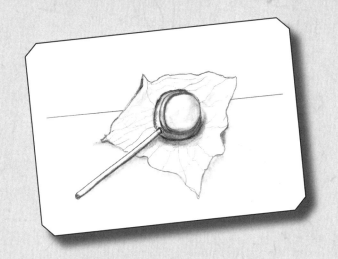

As Zeke opened the front door, he heard crying coming from the kitchen. There at the kitchen table sat his little brother, Dan. Mother held Danny's hand, and tears were running down his cheeks.

"Danny, I'm sorry you have a sliver, and I'm so sorry it hurts," Mother said. "But you must sit still so I can take it out."

Danny tried to pull his hand away and cried more loudly.

Zeke felt the sweet, purple lump in his pocket and looked at his little brother.

It is my lollipop, but a lollipop can take away tears, Zeke thought. A lollipop can keep Danny's other hand busy. A lollipop can help Mom take the sliver out faster.

Zeke pulled the lollipop from his pocket. Giving Danny my lollipop will make him happy, Zeke thought. And it will make me happy, too.

And that's what Zeke did to "visit the sick." What will *you* do when someone is sick or hurt?

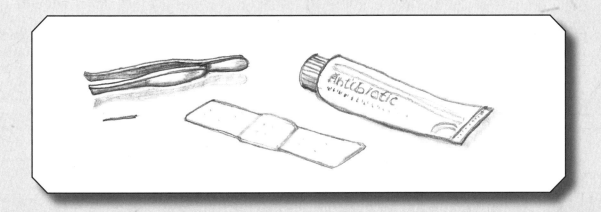

When someone is
sick or hurt, I can

11

What Can You Do to Shelter the Homeless?

Carlos and Nina's Idea

Carlos spit toothpaste into the bathroom sink. He looked into the mirror. Carlos smiled a toothless smile at himself.

"Look, Nina. Two teeth are gone. I can push my toothbrush into the empty space. I don't even have to open my mouth." Carlos grinned into the mirror.

"And I found two dollars under my pillow this morning. I am going to buy some candy. What are you going to buy with your tooth money?"

Nina reached across the sink. She held her toothbrush under the running water. "Well, I have saved my tooth money since last year, so I have six dollars.

"I was going to buy a sparkly blue necklace.

"But then I saw on TV that many children in Haiti live in tents. Their houses fell down in an earthquake and they have been living outside for a long time.

"They don't have bathrooms, or sinks to brush their teeth in or wash their hands." Nina dried her hands on the towel and followed Carlos to their bedrooms.

"A necklace is pretty. But I think people need safe houses a lot more than I need a necklace."

Carlos turned on the lamp in his bedroom. "If the children live in tents, they don't have soft beds and warm bedrooms." Carlos shook his head sadly. He took his piggy bank from the top of his dresser. "I can have candy another time. I want to help, too."

Carlos got into his warm bed. He wiggled another loose tooth. "Maybe if all my teeth fall out, they can make two houses."

And that's what Carlos and Nina did to shelter the homeless. What can *you* do to shelter the homeless?

When someone is
homeless, I can

12

What Can You Do to Instruct the Ignorant?

Jeremy's Idea

"Mommy, what is 'Spir-it-you-all' Works of Mercy? What is 'in-struct the ig-nor-ant'? I can't do this paper!

"Can you please help me with my school work?" Lily called from the kitchen table.

Mother put one last dish in the dishwasher.

She picked up two-year-old Joan. Then she sat down at the table between Jeremy and Lily.

"It says 'Spiritual Works of Mercy' at the top of the page. The first sentence says..."

"No, Joan, don't pull the tablecloth!"

Lily's school paper slid off the table and dropped to the floor.

"Joan do paper!" little Joan said. "Lily play with Joan!"

Mother turned to Jeremy. "I'm trying to help Lily, but little Joan wants to play.

"Can you please take a break from school work and play with Joan? Then I can help Lily with her paper."

"Sure, Mom." Jeremy stood up and took Joan by the hand. "Let's go upstairs and play. We can count steps on the way.

"Here is the first step. That's one."

"Wunnnnn," said Joan as she put her little foot on the first step.

"Two," said Jeremy as he helped Joan up the next step.

"Tooooooooo!" copied Joan.

"Now, three."

Joan did a little dance on the next step.

"Fweeeeeeeee!"

"Hey, Mom, Lily isn't the only one learning about the Spiritual Works of Mercy," grinned Jeremy.

"I'm instructing the ignorant, too!"

13

What Can You Do to Instruct the Ignorant?

Sara's Idea

"Sara, you know that Mr. Moore grew pumpkins in his garden this summer. Now that it's fall, the pumpkins are big and ripe.

"If you can cross the street carefully, Mr. Moore says he has a big pumpkin for you."

"Oh, yes, I can be careful!" Sara ran to get

her jacket from the front closet.

"Me, too!" four-year-old Pete cried. "I want to go, too! I want to help get a pumpkin!"

Mother thought a minute. "I don't know, Pete. Sometimes you don't listen. Can you obey Sara and cross the street carefully?"

"Oh, yes, Mama." Pete nodded his head up and down, up and down. "I will obey. I will listen to Sara. I will hold her hand."

Pete grabbed Sara's hand, and the two children were soon stopped at the side of the street.

Pete tugged Sara's hand as a car zoomed past. "Come on! Let's get the pumpkin!"

"Not yet, Pete. It is not safe yet. First, we stop. Then we look both ways. Then we listen for cars that we can't see."

"O.K.," Pete agreed. "I am looking both ways. I don't see any cars. Let's go!" Pete started to step into the street.

"Not yet, Pete. Listen! I hear another car, coming fast around the corner!" Sara held Pete's hand firmly as a car zoomed past.

Pete's eyes opened wide. He moved closer to his big sister. "That car was too speedy. I do not want to be squished on the street.

"I am glad you told me how to stop, look, and listen."

And that is how Sara instructed the ignorant. How can *you* instruct the ignorant?

When someone is
ignorant, I can

14

What Can You Do to Admonish the Sinner?

Andy's Idea

"Steven, why are you hiding in my closet?" ten-year-old Andy asked his brother.

"Well," Steven whispered, "you know Mom's short rose bush by the driveway, the one I ran over with my bike last month?"

"You mean the rose bush that Mom said not to ride your bike around any more?"

"That's the one," nodded Steven. "I didn't mean to, but I ran over it again. Now it is even shorter. Please don't tell."

"Steven, you need to tell Mom the truth. If you tell her she will understand. She will not be too mad."

"Yes, she will," Steven sniffed. "I will be in bad trouble. Maybe I can tell her that Dad drove the car over it."

"No, that is a lie. Lying is a sin. You already disobeyed, and lying will make it worse. Just go tell her."

"But she will take my bike away," Steven gulped.

"Maybe. And she will probably tell you to be more careful. But even when it is hard, we must tell the truth.

"Telling the truth pleases God, and I promise that it will please Mom, too." Andy gently pulled his little brother to his feet.

"Come on. I will go with you. We can tell Mom together."

And that is how Andy admonished the sinner.

15

What Can You Do to Admonish the Sinner?

Rose's Idea

"But it's my turn!" Justin tugged hard on the trike's handlebars.

"No!" screamed four-year-old Kate. She began to kick at Justin. "No! Go away!"

"Ow! Quit it! That hurts!" Justin tugged again at the handlebars. "Don't kick me!

"Rose," Justin yelled to his big sister, "Kate won't share. She's kicking me. Make her stop!"

"But Justin never gives me a turn," Kate wailed from her seat on the trike.

Rose put the book she was reading down on the porch. "Kate, I am surprised at you.

"How can you kick Justin, your very own brother? And Justin, how can you forget to share with your little sister?

"God made us a family, to be kind to one another and help each other win Heaven."

"But she won't give me a turn!" Justin pouted.

"Maybe," Rose said, "she won't give you a turn because of your bad example.

"If you are kind to Kate, and set a good example, maybe she will want to share."

"And Kate, you must not kick Justin. Perhaps if you are kind, he will let you have more turns.

"Now, I have an idea. Justin, you are strong. You can pedal the trike with Kate on the back step.

"See the step on the back of the trike, Kate? You can stand here. Put your arms around Justin's waist and hold on."

Kate stood on the step and put her arms around Justin's waist. "I am sorry I kicked you. And I am glad God gave me a big brother."

"And I am sorry I didn't share very well," Justin said as he began to pedal. "But we can have fun together now."

And that is what happened when Rose admonished sinners.

16

What Can You Do to Admonish the Sinner?

Paul's Idea

"Vrooom! Vrooom!" Tom sat on the sandpile, running his toy truck up a hill of sand. "See how fast my truck is!"

"Vrooom, vrooom! Race you to the top of the hill!" Paul pushed his truck up the sand hill next to Tom's truck.

New words: guess   answer

"Tom! Tom! Where are you?" Tom's grandma called from next door. "Tom, it's time for lunch. Tom!" The voice stopped and a door closed.

"Hey, didn't you hear your grandma?" Paul asked. "You are supposed to go home at lunch time.

"Why didn't you answer your grandma when she called?"

"Aw," grumbled Tom, "I don't want to go home yet. Playing with trucks is better."

Paul was shocked. "But you need to obey your grandma! That is the best thing to do."

Tom looked at his house. He looked at Paul. He stood up and shook the sand off his toy truck. "Maybe if I hurry home now, I can come back after lunch. I guess it is best to obey."

"It sure is!" Paul waved as Tom ran for home. "See you after lunch, if it's O.K. with your grandma!"

And that is what happened when Paul admonished the sinner.

17

What Can You Do to Admonish the Sinner?

Luke's Idea

"So how was Sunday School, boys?" Dad asked as they drove home from church.

"Oh, it was fine," Mark answered. "Except I had to sit by that girl Anna. Her dress was all dirty, and sometimes she smells. I told her that I don't like to sit by her."

"What a mean thing to say!" Luke leaned

across the back seat and poked Mark with his finger. "You know, sometimes you smell, too. Anna is really nice, and I like her."

"Thank you, Luke," Dad said. "Mark, you need to tell Anna you are sorry for saying such a thing.

"When Anna was baptized, she became a child of God just as you did when you were baptized. It isn't how others look on the outside. We need to look for Jesus on the inside."

"Well, it's hard to see what's inside," Mark said, "but I can see her dirty dress outside."

"Huh! Remember when you wore the same shirt all week?" Luke offered. "You were dirty, too.

"Our teacher said God deeply loves all His children. He lives inside Anna, and He lives inside you. It isn't what is on the outside, but Who is on the inside."

"I remember now," Mark answered slowly. "Next time I sit by Anna, I will think of Jesus inside. Why, that means I get to sit next to Jesus!"

I can admonish the
sinner by

18

What Can You Do to Counsel the Doubtful?

Gabe's Idea

"Hang on, Dominic!" yelled Gabe as he pushed the merry-go-round faster and faster. "Don't get dizzy and fall off!"

Gabe jumped onto the merry-go-round as it spun in a dizzy circle.

"This is fun. I'm glad we live by the park," said

Dominic, "and I'm glad you live next door. We can play together every day."

"Yes, it is fun to live next door," agreed Gabe. "I like it when you come to my house, and I like it when I go to your house. You are my good friend.

"And we even get to go to Holy Mass together!"

"Yes, but I'd rather go to the park sometimes." Dominic dragged his feet in the dirt under the spinning merry-go-round.

"Why do we have to go to Mass every Sunday, anyway? I don't get it."

"Oh, that's easy." Gabe jumped off and started to push the merry-go-round again. "We are best friends, aren't we?"

Dominic nodded. "Of course, but what does that have to do with Mass?"

"Well, best friends like to talk to each other. They like to spend time at each other's house. And then they go home happy."

Will you spend an hour with Me? Come, tell Me your joys and sorrows! I will welcome you tenderly!

Gabe pulled himself onto the spinning merry-go-round again.

"When we go to Holy Mass, I remember that my very best Friend is there. He invites me to come to His house, to talk to Him and spend time together. Then I go home happy.

"And when I'm eight, He will come to me in Holy Communion. I'm glad the Church reminds us to visit our best Friend every Sunday."

And that is how Gabe counseled the doubtful.

19

What Can You Do to Counsel the Doubtful?

Ray looked sadly out the window at the rain pouring down. "I guess this means we won't go to the beach today. And no beach means no picnic.

"And I prayed so hard for sunshine, too."

"Cheer up!" Elian patted his friend on the shoulder. "Maybe it will be sunny tomorrow and we will go then."

"Maybe," Ray said sadly. "But we can't go now. I don't think God heard my prayers. Do you think God really answers prayer?"

"Oh, I know so," Elian answered.

"My mom and dad used to be very sad because they didn't have any kids. They prayed and prayed for my mom to have a baby.

"But she didn't have a baby."

"You mean," asked Ray, "that God didn't answer their prayers?"

"Oh, no. God answered their prayers. He just had a better way," smiled Elian.

"What do you mean?" Ray was puzzled.

Elian smiled happily. "God said, 'No baby.' Instead, He sent Me! I was three years old when they adopted me.

"Dad says I'm the best answer to prayer they ever had.

"That's why they named me Elian, because Elian means, 'God answers.'"

And that is how Elian counseled the doubtful. What can *you* do to counsel the doubtful?

I can counsel the
doubtful by

20

What Will You Do to Pray for the Living and the Dead?

Todd's Idea

Todd waved at the airplane as it roared over his house. He watched the plane rise up, up into the evening sky, growing smaller and smaller.

Todd and his family lived on a military base, a special town for soldiers and their families.

New words: soldier   weapon

The military base also had an airport, and lots of planes. Todd knew that the plane he had seen carried brave soldiers, just like his dad.

Perhaps the soldiers on the plane were going to another base. Or maybe the soldiers were being sent to do a brave and dangerous job.

Todd reached into his pocket. He pulled out the rosary that his dad had given him just before he, too, had left on a plane. The rosary was just like the one his dad carried always.

When his dad gave the rosary to Todd, his dad had smiled and said,

"St. Pio called the rosary his strong weapon.

"With this rosary you can be a brave soldier of Christ."

Todd quietly began to pray. "My Jesus, I offer this rosary for all the brave soldiers on that plane, and for their families.

"And I pray for the souls of soldiers long ago. They gave their lives to keep us free."

And that is how Todd prayed for the living and the dead. How will *you* pray for the living and the dead?

I can pray for
the living and the
dead by

21

How Will You Forgive Injuries?

Cassie ran up the porch steps, tears streaming down her cheeks.

"Daddy, Daddy," she sobbed. "Just look at what Jenny did!"

Dad turned from painting the front door and set his paintbrush across the paint bucket. "What happened, Cassie?"

Cassie held her favorite baby doll, Polly, close to her chest. "Jenny pulled Polly's arm off," sobbed Cassie, "and here it is!"

"I am not going to play at Jenny's house any more." Cassie handed poor Polly's arm to her Daddy. "I don't like Jenny at all."

"There, there." Dad set Polly's arm on the porch rail. He gave Cassie

a big hug. "I think Doctor Dad can fix poor Polly.

"But there is something that needs fixing even more. You need to forgive Jenny, just as our good God forgives you."

Cassie sniffed and shook her head. "But she broke Polly and made me sad."

"Yes," agreed Dad. "And sometimes you make others sad. Sometimes it is our job to forgive, and sometimes we need to be forgiven."

Dad twisted Polly's arm back into place. "There! As good as new.

"Now, what kind thing can you do for Jenny, to show you have forgiven her?"

"Oh, thank you, Daddy!" Cassie hugged Polly to her heart. "I will forgive Jenny. I will ask her to come play dolls with me."

"Good job," Dad smiled. "All fixed."

And that is how Cassie forgave injuries. How will *you* forgive injuries?

22

How Will You Forgive Injuries?

Thump! The back yard teeter-totter bumped to a stop on the hard ground.

"Ouch! Cut it out, Rick," Jerome yelled to his brother. "You don't have to come down so hard!"

"Aw, I was just having fun." Rick gave another leap at his end of the teeter-totter.

Bump! Jerome banged down hard on the seat again. "That's it! I'm going in the house!

"Rick is a mean brother," Jerome mumbled to himself. He went into the boys' bedroom, shut the door, and threw himself down on the bed.

Then Jerome looked up at the crucifix on the wall.

People were pretty mean to Jesus, too, Jerome thought to himself. They nailed Him to the cross, but still He loved them. And He forgave the people who hurt Him.

"Jesus, please help me forgive Rick," Jerome prayed. "You were hurt a lot more, but You still loved.

"Help me think of all the good stuff Rick does, not just the mean stuff. I forgive him. Now, please help me love him. Amen."

Jerome opened his eyes. He looked at Rick's bed on the other side of the room. Sitting folded on top of the bed were the clean sheets Mom had put there.

The clean sheets gave Jerome an idea. Rick sure hates to make his bed, Jerome thought. This makes me think of something Father Tony said.

Father Tony says love isn't how we feel. Love is what we do. I will do something kind for Rick.

I can love and I can forgive. I will make Rick's bed for him.

And that is just what Jerome did.

23

How Will You Forgive Injuries?

Mary sat at the breakfast table with her head down.

"Why so sad, dear heart?" Mom asked as she filled the glasses with milk. "Don't you like your toast this morning?"

Mary picked her toast up and took a teeny bite. "I like the toast. But I like birthday parties better." A tear slipped down the end of Mary's nose.

"What day is this?" Mom looked surprised. "Did we forget your birthday?"

"No, Mommy. You know Clare, next door. It is her birthday." Mary wiped her eyes with her napkin.

"Clare invited everyone to her birthday party, except for me."

"Ah, so that's why my girl is sad. It seems that Clare has forgotten you. Your feelings are hurt."

Mom looked tenderly at Mary. "Can you be kind to Clare, even if Clare has not been kind to you?"

Mary started to shake her head. Then she slowly nodded. "Yes, Mommy."

"Good. Maybe we can have a little tea party here for a few girls." Mom put two more slices of toast in the toaster. "Can you think of someone to invite?"

"Oh, yes!" Mary beamed. "I will invite Sara, and Jenna, and..." Mary thought for a minute. "...and Clare!"

And that is how Mary forgave injuries. How will *you* forgive injuries?

I will forgive

injuries by

24

How Will You Bear Wrongs Patiently?

Jakob's Idea

Jakob set the marking pen on the desk next to his drawing. He held the picture up for his little brother to see. "See, Jordan? It is a deer, like the deer Grandpa feeds in his back yard."

Jordan pulled his chubby baby fingers out of his mouth and pointed. "Pitty deer. Ganpa deer."

New words: wrongs   patient   patiently

"Yes, 'Ganpa deer.' This is for Grandpa's birthday." Jakob set his drawing back on the desk. "Now, don't touch," Jakob ordered. "I need to go set the table."

A minute later, as Jakob set forks in place, he heard the sound of tearing paper.

He turned to see Jordan, waving pieces of Jakob's picture.

"Pitty deer!" Jordan proudly gave the torn pieces to Jakob. "Pitty deer!"

Jakob groaned. "Yah, 'pity deer,' is the truth." He stared at what was left of his drawing. Then he saw the baby smile on his brother's face.

"It is hard to be patient with you, little brother, but love makes everything easier, like Dad says." Jakob picked up the giggling baby and swung him in a circle.

"I can always make another picture for Grandpa, but God only made one Jordan."

And that is how Jakob bore wrongs patiently. How will *you* bear wrongs patiently?

25

How Will You Bear Wrongs Patiently?

Kady's Idea

Peter handed the dish towel to Kady. "Mom says it's my turn to wash and your turn to dry."

Kady frowned as she took the towel from Peter's soapy hand.

"Why the sour pickle face?" he asked.

"Oh, it's Patsy," Kady grunted. "She was rude to me."

"You mean Patsy, your best friend?"

"Yes, Patsy. When I said 'hi' to her at the store today, she didn't say anything." Kady frowned. "That was rude.

"She just walked past with her Daddy. Patsy didn't even look at me."

Peter handed a dripping plate to his sister. "Well, maybe she didn't see you. Things aren't always as they seem.

"Maybe Patsy was upset about something. Maybe she had a rock in her shoe, or a fly in her nose."

Kady giggled. "Or maybe she had lemons for breakfast." Kady took a cup from the drainer. "I get it.

"It's like that verse about Jesus dying for us, even when we were sinners.* He still loves, even if people don't love back."

"What's this about Patsy?" Mom asked as she came into the kitchen. "Did you know that her mother is in the hospital? We need to pray for her."

"Now I know why she didn't look at me!" Kady said softly. "Patsy wasn't rude, she was worried! From now on, I will try to think the best of people, not the worst.

"Mom, when we finish dishes, may we bake cookies for Patsy's family?"

"I think that's a fine idea," Mom replied. "What shall we put in the cookies? Chocolate chips? Peanuts?"

Kady giggled. "Anything but sour pickles."

And that is how Kady bore wrongs patiently. How will *you* bear wrongs patiently?

I will bear wrongs

patiently by